" ...*It was in Argentina where I ate the best meat ever. It is of excellent quality and the most tender in the world. I believe this is due to the quality of their genetics and their environment. It is absolutely superb in all the ways it is prepared.* "

Mr. Bill Bunce,
Director Agribusiness Division,
Estado de Wyoming, USA

Other titles published by Maizal

Español/Spanish
El Mate
El Tango
El Gaucho
Argentina Natural
La Cocina Argentina
Indígenas Argentinos
Vinos Argentinos
Carne Argentina
Textiles Argentinos

Inglés/English
The Mate
The Tango
The Gaucho
Argentine Nature
Argentine Cookery
Argentine Indians
Argentine Wines
Argentine Textiles

Bilingüe/Bilingual
Teatro Colón/
Colón Theatre
Pintura Argentina/
Argentine Painting

Argentrip
Argentina's on-line travel guide
www.argentrip.com

© Máximo J. Ayerza, 2001
Diseño: Christian le Comte and Sophie le Comte
Translation: Mónica G. Hoss de le Comte
Hecho el depósito que previene la ley 11.723
ISBN 987-9479-08-4
Published by Maizal
Muñiz 438, B1640FDB, Martínez
Buenos Aires, Argentina.
E-mail: info@maizal.com
www.maizal.com
Printed in August 2004 by Morgan Internacional

Máximo J. Ayerza

Argentine Beef

MAIZAL
EDICIONES

The Animals

The Spanish conquerors brought the first bovine animals to Argentina in 1552; they were seven cows and a bull and they were brought from Paraguay.

All the livestock brought to the Río de la Plata during the sixteenth century were of Spanish origin, that is, of the Iberian type, especially Castilian and Andalusian races, from central and southern Spain, from the neighbouring districts of the ports from where the ships left for the New World.

Moritz Rugendas (1802-1858) "Bull"

These animals descend from the longhorn Hamitic cattle, domesticated in Egypt about BC 4000 and taken to Spain from northern Africa.

Used mainly as draft animals, they were not bred for their meat or their milk. At that time, commerce did not demand any other qualities than those these animals had, that is the reason why they continued reproducing themselves without any purpose of improvement.

The Pampas were soon occupied by these cattle and since they could not be retained because of their character, they roamed the Pampas, multiplying in freedom and adapting themselves to the favourable environment. Our Criollo race, which so closely resembles the cattle introduced by the Spaniards, developed from these animals.

Jorge Schulte "Herdsmen"

They can still be found in the North of the country, in mountain areas and in scrublands of scarce vegetation.

The first vaquerías (primitive farms) were created at that time. On these farms, the animals were caught in the field only for their leather, which was exported to Europe.

Egyptian Bull engraved on a slate tablet. First Dynasty

The rest of the animal was left to rot in the field. It was also fairly common that the gauchos (nomadic horsemen of the Pampas) slaughtered the animals with the only purpose of eating their tongues.

The commercial activity began in 1602, with the creation of the *saladeros* (places where meat was salted in order to preserve it) that devoted themselves to the production of *tasajo* (dried or jerked meat). Meat was cut into long and thin pieces and then salted and pressed to extract its juice. The first tasajo shipment was sent to Cuba. It was sold to the merchants who brought slaves to the Río de la Plata.

"Tarquin"
Engraving, nineteenth century

Not only *tasajo* was exported, but leather and tallow were exported as well. The demand for these articles was even greater than the demand for meat. The leather, *tasajo* and tallow trade was carried on until 1824.

With the first introduction of British animals, in 1823, a new era of cattle raising began in Argentina.

The animals brought from Britain belonged to the small red bodied Celtic race, which had been used as draft animals, and which had been crossed on cattle from northern Italy and Gaul and taken to Britain by the Romans. In Britain these animals were crossed with bigger animals introduced during the Scandinavian invasions and then finally crossed on animals brought by the Normans. The cattle resulting from all these crossings are probably the ancestors of the current Shorthorn breed.

Anonimous (c. 1787)
"Paisanos or Camiluchos (horsemen)"

Little is known about the breeding methods used at that time, but it is known that the breeders preferred animals raised for meat and milk, to the bigger animals bred for draft.

This, no doubt, determined the methodology used in order to keep animals solely for beef and milk production. In 1823, the English John Miller introduced the first Shorthorn bull to Argentina. It was

Charles H. Pellegrini (1800-1875) "Processing Plant", c.1830

called Tarquin. This bull imprinted type and increase in the rate of weight gain and mature size to our *Criollo* livestock, and its descendants, who bore these lasting characteristic marks, were known under the name of "Tarquinos".

During the first decades of the twentieth century, the first meat processing plants were established; at the very beginning, most of them were in British hands, later on they were sold to American companies.

The investigations into the refrigeration industry made by Charles Tellier (1828-1913) were applied to the ships that transported meat. This, together with the achievements of the meat processing plants, made it possible for Argentina to export its excellent quality meat, not only to all European markets, but to those of the rest of the world as well and contributed to the economic and social development of the country.

Breeds

Shorthorn

Hereford

Aberdeen Angus

Zebu

Santa Gertrudis

The import of stud bulls from the United Kingdom at the end of the nineteenth century did not stop until the first quarter of the twentieth century. Even during the war, excellent bulls continued being brought by Argentine stockbreeders.

As mentioned above, John Miller imported the Shorthorn bull "Tarquin" in 1823; then Guillermo White introduced again several **Shorthorn** bulls in 1848; in 1862 Leonardo Pereyra introduced a **Hereford** bull called "Niagara".

In 1879, Carlos Guerrero brought "Virtuoso", an **Aberdeen Angus** bull.

There is no denying that Great Britain has made a major contribution to the excellence of Argentine livestock, not only selling these stud bulls to Argentine stockbreeders, but buying our meat in big quantities, so that the native *estancieros* (farm owners) diligently embarked on improving their livestock.

In 1941, **Zebu** cattle were brought to Argentina and were crossed on the traditional British meat cattle with the purpose of achieving a better adaptation of these animals to the subtropical regions in the North of the country.

As time went by, the crossing of these races originated the **Santa Gertrudis**, **Brangus** and **Braford** breeds, which are the resulting breeds of crossing Zebu cattle on Shorthorn, Aberdeen Angus and Hereford respectively. The Indian Zebu was also crossed on Criollo cattle. From 1960 on, a growing interest for Continental breeds started, especially for the **Charolais** breed imported from France. The Charolais is a very heavy animal which, crossed on British breeds, produces very lean meat.

In 1966, several stockbreeders started importing the French **Limousin** breed. As with the Charolais, the Limousin was crossed on British breeds and they also produce lean meat. The crossing on the Aberdeen Angus cattle has generated a breed called Limangus.

Brangus

Braford

In 1967, the German **Fleckvieh** breed was imported and was also crossed on other races.

Although many breeds, native to different countries, have been brought and crossed, Argentine livestock continues being mainly British.

Charolais

The current predominant breeds are Aberdeen Angus and Hereford, and the crossing among them. Argentina is considered the biggest reservoir of pure British cattle in the world because of the quality and quantity of the purebreds kept in our large grazing areas.

Limousin

It is evident that the modern Argentine breeder has the same nerve his ancestors had, and he spares no effort to maintain a high level in cattle raising. He is admired by breeders the whole world over.

Fleckvieh

The Pampas

The word Pampa is probably of Quechua origin. It means flat land, plain.

The Pampa is a green sea of grass that occupies a third of the total surface of Argentina, and it is the ideal place to breed cattle.

Home of the legendary *Gaucho*, it is a boundless horizon, a plain with natural pastures or sown with lucerne, wheat, corn, soy and sunflower.

The Pampas have excellent climate and soil conditions, a perfect combination that is very rare to find anywhere else in the world.

The climate is mild, with an average annual temperature between 12 °C and 18 °C. Rainfall, which is evenly distributed along the year, varies from 500 to 1000 mm. There are no raging storms or very long droughts.

The territory taken from the Indians covered a small portion of the Province of Buenos Aires. The South of the Provinces of Córdoba and Santa Fe, and most of the Provinces of Entre Ríos and Corrientes were either occupied by Indians or lay abandoned.

This even temperature provides excellent conditions for cattle grazing throughout the year without need for shelter.

During the colonial period, cattle were raised in a very small area around the city of Buenos Aires and the livestock were rounded up every evening (rodeo system) to prevent the animals from escaping into the immense plain.

Later on, agricultural work was extended not only to the whole Province of Buenos Aires but to the provinces in the North and in the Northeast as well. The Province of Buenos Aires was the hub of all this activity because of two circumstances: the vicinity of the port of Buenos Aires, and the constant fight against the Indians who did not stop harassing the small settlements, thinly scattered in the huge plain.

In the first decades of the nineteenth century, the primitive frontier line remained invariable, although several expeditions had already been sent with the intention of evicting the Indians.

The first expedition, at the beginning of the 1820s, was led by Martin Rodríguez, the second was organised by military forces from Santa Fe, Córdoba and Cuyo and got as far as the riverbanks of the Río Colorado (Red River), but they returned without having consolidated their new positions.

Hereford breed bulls

In 1862, the country was temporarily at peace but the fight against the *malones* started again. The *malón* was the surprise attack of the Indians who sacked the frontier area.

Around 1870, Doctor Adolfo Alsina ordered a wide ditch to be dug along the frontier to stop these attacks. He also established a line of outposts that started in the south of the Province of Buenos Aires. But the Indians with their *malones* went on pestering the incipient settlements, destroying everything they found on their way, taking with them not only cattle but also many white women, who were held captive in their *tolderías* (Indian camps).

It was in the year 1882 that the Pampas together with the South of the Province of Santa Fe and Córdoba, were pacified. General Julio A. Roca not only "conquered the desert" but also closed the mountain passes of the Andes to stop the belligerent tribes from crossing from Chile.

Prilidiano Pueyrredón
(1823-1870)
"Herds"

Estancias and Estancieros

The land given to the people who accompanied Juan de Garay when founding Buenos Aires in 1580 where the beginning of a slow and gradual formation of estancias.

First Cattle Mark registred in 1589; it belonged to Francisco Salas Videla.

At the beginning of the nineteenth century, most of the land taken from the Indians during the war, was still fiscal property. It was precisely at that time when it started being sold. The Governor Juan Manuel de Rosas sold 1.500 leagues (1 league = 5 square kilometres) of virgin land, situated between the Río Salado (Salado River) and the coast of the Province of Buenos Aires. The colonisation of this land, bought at a very low price, and in large stretches, developed very slowly and involved a high degree of risk. At the beginning of 1850, when a new civil war was on the verge of breaking out, the Indians started attacking the settlements along the frontier.

At that time, British breeders who had settled along the right riverbank of the Río de la Plata, began crossing their cattle on pedigree animals brought from Great Britain. But everything was still very primitive in the land of the future *estancias* (large Argentine farms).

The huge stretches of land were not fenced. This made the development of stockbreeding, or any other agricultural work, little less than impossible. Incipient fencing was started as late as 1845.

Once the "desert" had been conquered, private property extended considerably in an area of the Province of Buenos Aires where today the best *cabañas* (cattle breeding farms) are found. The government sold an extension of 3.300.000 hectares in order to pay for the expenses caused by military campaigns.

Many farm tenants who had established themselves in the North became landowners of the Province of Buenos Aires when they bought the plots of land that the government was auctioning.

These new landowners abandoned their farms in the North, where they had started agricultural

Juan Manuel Blanes (1830-1901) "Herds"

settlements and went southwards driving their herds and taking with them the scanty gear and work equipment they possessed.

Carried away by their enthusiasm and ready to spare no effort to develop the newly acquired land, they soon learnt of the overwhelming magnitude of the task that they were facing.

They had left behind their farms and their settlements, and entered a never ending desert that seemed totally barren, without trees in the immensity of the horizon, with very few natural watering holes, and with no resources and no means of communication. There was nothing at all, not even trees to built their houses with. They had kindled the hope that there might be a possibility of acquiring, in the distant settlements, the necessary elements for the construction of their houses and fence posts to delimit *corrales* (stockyards) and *potreros* (grazing fields), but they soon learnt that that was impossible. These settlements were way too far and the freight was too expensive.

Branding irons are still used today since they are the best way of indentifying cattle property.

Emeric Essex Vidal (1971-1961) "Slaughterhouse"

There was just straw, earth and leather and these were the elements they used.

In order to build their huts, they used *huasquilla* (long strip of hide) to sew the pieces of leather together, the same way the Indians did.

Others lived under the carts in which they had carried their belongings.

J. Aguyari(1843-1885) "Countryside in San Nicolás de los Arroyos"

Once established, they started with all sorts of rural activities, they had to round up their animals every evening and look for lost animals so that little by little the cattle got accustomed to their new habitat.

Since there were no posts to mark the limits of their grazing fields, as a makeshift, they dug two concentric ditches using the earth to form an embankment thus preventing the animals from escaping.

There was an entrance to this improvised *corral*: two posts marked the place where it was possible to cross the ditch. A long rope was stretched between the posts and the skins of foxes, pumas and other animals caught nearby, were hung from the rope to instil fear into their cattle.

In this hostile atmosphere, the Pampas were slowly conquered and peopled. The farms that had been abandoned in the North were left with practically no cattle. It was then, that a new era in the evolution of those primitive farms began. These farms eventually became modern *cabañas* (breeding farms). This evolution was possible because of two factors: the farmers started fencing their land and windmills were set up in order to pump water.

There were no farm labourers, this, together with the harshness of their work, the inclemency of the weather, and their own unease resulting from the immensity that surrounded their rudimentary farm, contributed to fill them with a terrible sense of anguish.

A. de la Valle (1852-1903) "Separating" (detail)

Cattle Branding

*Title page of the
General Collection of
Cattle Brands,
Hipólito Bacle,
1830*

Cattle mark

*Albert Adam
(1801-1866), after
J. D. Dulin
"Slaughter-house,
Buenos Aires"*

The practice of identifying the property of livestock, marking it with a burning iron, was started as early as Buenos Aires was founded.

Due to the lack of fences, the method was of primary importance to keep the herds apart. In 1589 the first cattle mark was registered in the Town Council of Buenos Aires in order to protect the produce of this new activity. It did not take long for the system to spread to other regions.

In 1775, the Town Council of Buenos Aires ordered the farmers to enter all the signs used, to be able to publish a master book with all available brands and provide the Provincial Mayor and the Representative of the farmers with a catalogue to protect their cattle from rustlers.

The arbitrariness of the drawings of these brands, lacking any regulation and just following the whims

of the farmers caused great confusion when the cattle had to be separated. If in doubt, the farmers used to consult experts who were "intelligent in marks" as they were called at that time.

A European writer, the German Sigwart Blum, ponders with admiration and certain astonishment about the rich variety and perfection of these marks, which have been used for more than four hundred years in the Argentine countryside.

He says, "From the graphic point of view, these brands are ideal signs of visual identification. This is also due to a technical factor, because burning with an iron does not admit marks that have double contours or thick lines. This heraldry is made up of monograms with the first and last name of the farmer. Numbers and drawings of fauna and flora can also be found; they do not even lack mythical symbols (hearts, hands, crosses, etc.) or runic signs."

In 1825, time had come for a regulation that would ensure the protection of the source of this new wealth. On July 22, a decree was signed by the Head of the Government Bernardino Rivadavia which provided that the Police Department was to be held responsible for the publication of an annual catalogue of cattle brands of the Province of Buenos Aires, including the districts and the names of the people that used them.

This of course was very difficult, not only because of the immense variety of brands, but because of the graphic production difficulties of the time.

In November 1828, the Swiss lithographer Hipólito Bacle arrived in Buenos Aires and in March 1929 he offered his service to the Government. In January 1834, Bacle could finally start with "The General Collection of Cattle Brands of the Province of Buenos Aires".

Cattle mark

Fencing

Among the many factors that more powerfully contributed to the evolution of Argentine rural areas, there are three that influenced it significantly although in different ways: fencing, the importation of pure-bred stocks and the progressive development of the meat industry.

María Luisa Cristofoletti De Servi (1890-1982) "Corner Post"

By fencing off their properties, the farmers not only separated their fields from their neighbours', but they started dividing their farms into grazing fields and stockyards. Fencing also allowed an improvement of their livestock because they were able to classify and divide their cattle into different categories.

Fencing was of utmost importance for the improvement of cattle breeding at the beginning of the twentieth century.

In colonial times and in the first years of Argentine independence, cattle were raised out in the open and the farmers never knew for sure who the cattle belonged to.

The first demarcation system was carried out by means of ditches but this method was not very effective. Then, thorny bushes were used but this system was not effective either, due to the immense extensions of the fields.

Richard Newton introduced the wire fence in 1845, but he only wired off five hectares that included the house, a small wood and the vegetable garden of his farm "Santa María".

The first farmer who fenced off his entire *estancia* was the German Francisco Halbach in 1855. His farm was called "Los Remedios" and it was in Cañuelas in the Province of Buenos Aires.

Argentine postage stamp, 1942

After this beginning, the introduction of wire fence was only slowly carried out in spite of President Domingo F. Sarmiento's insistence with which he tried to convince the farmers to do it. "Secure your fortune," he used to say. The farmers answered that their animals did not really get lost, because someone would eventually take advantage of them.

The expansion of the system of fencing off the fields was slow, partly due to its high cost, and partly because of a psychological reason, derived from the native farmers' natural inclination to reject all elements that could hinder their natural freedom of movement.

Fencing was accepted well after the "Conquest of the Desert" in 1880.

Up to then, the farmers left their agricultural properties in the hands of Divine Providence. The activities on the farms were just the daily rodeos; giving water to their animals when this was possible; curing some illnesses, branding and castrating.

Advertisement in an Estanciero Journal, 1882

As a consequence, the task of improving and selecting livestock was utopian, because all animals of the same species were left grazing together, bulls, cows, calves, heifers and young castrated bulls.

Under these circumstances, it was impossible not only to start a selective process that could lead to modern cattle raising, but to be able to organise an appropriate rate of reproduction as well.

Cattle-breeding Farm

The *cabaña* (cattle-breeding farm) has been an enterprise that has greatly contributed to the development and improvement of Argentine livestock.

Cabaña is the name given to the establishment which devotes itself to the raising of pedigree cattle with excellent genealogical and production records. The *cabañas* have produced and developed the use of high quality breeding animals, especially pedigree bulls and cows.

Commercial breeders buy these animals in order to improve their herds.

At the beginning, the *cabañeros* produced bulls for their own herds and then they started to sell their surplus to commercial breeders.

These animals had a special feeding method and lived in special sheds with 10 or 12 individual boxes.

Every year, breeders incorporate animals from breeding farms into their herds. This grately contributes to develop the production of meat in Argentina.

Today these animals are bred in the open and are fed on grass to which dry hay and grain are added.

Although stockyards are still used for individual insemination of cows, today the techniques of artificial insemination and embryon transplants are the methods most widely used.

Genealogy and ancestry together with physical appearance are the selection standards that have been carefully applied and the results are at hand.

These two factors have been taken into account since the cattle breeding farms started the process of selective breeding.

Production

The *cabaña*, breeding and *invernada* (fattening) are the bases of cattle production.

Commercial breeders buy the bulls in order to produce calves that will then be bought by *inverna-*

*Prilidiano Pueyrredón
(1823-1870)
"The stockyards"*

dores (people in charge of cattle fattening). Once the calves have been fattened and they have become steers, they will be taken to market and then to the meat processing plant. From there they will be distributed in the retail market or exported.

Invernada or cattle fattening is the process by which the animals are transformed into first quality meat for the market.

In winter they generally receive an addition of dry grass, hay and, lately, maize grain which has made it possible to shorten the fattening period.

Argentina is one of the best places for fattening cattle since the natural conditions of the country foster a pastoral system with natural pastures or in fields sown with lucerne and barley.

From the large stock of approximately 49 million animals, 12 million are annually slaughtered.

Exhibitions

Argentine Rural Society

The first international exhibition was held in 1885 with 894 breeding animals, 220 of which were imported from different European countries.

First prizes at the Argentine Rural Society

The first Rural Exhibition took place in 1875, in a big vacant lot on the corner of the streets Florida and Paraguay, in the City of Buenos Aires. Its owner Leonardo Pereyra generously offered it to the "Sociedad Rural Argentina" (Argentine Rural Society).

In spite of the meagre means of its organisers, the exhibition was inaugurated on April 11th, 1875 and called everybody's attention, especially that of the authorities.

Don Nicolás Avellaneda, the President of Argentina, and the Governor of the Province of Buenos Aires, Don Carlos Casares did not miss the opening day. It was visited by 18.000 people.

In this exhibition of agricultural products, 66 horses, 13 bovine animals, 74 sheep, 16 goats, 15 dogs and 19 groups of poultry and rabbits were shown. On the last day, it was announced that the next show would be held at the Parque Tres de Febrero in Palermo to the North of the City of Buenos Aires. But for political and economic reasons, the exhibition organised in 1876 was poorly visited. Palermo was at that time far from the centre of the city and in the middle of boggy moorlands where it was not easy to build the storehouses. In 1878, 313 head of cattle were exhibited and for the first time 158 pieces of agricultural machinery were also shown.

At the end of the nineteenth and the beginning of the twentieth century, the pavilions, which are still used, were built in Palermo, where the "Rural" has been held ever since. These yearly exhibitions have become a tradition in Argentine agriculture.

Cattle Market

In 1590, Juan de Garay established the "Corrales del Abasto", the supply market of Buenos Aires, in what today is the centre of the city. In 1607, a decree of the Town Council mentioned the construction of "a stockyard for the city", which was also going to be used as public butchery or slaughterhouse.

Livestock brought to the city was slaughtered in this yard and the meat was sold in the market opposite the Royal Fort. In 1775, livestock was burdened with a tax of half a *real* per head.

In March 1900, the *Mercado Municipal de Hacienda* (Municipal Livestock Market) was established in Liniers. Here the animals are received, unloaded and after verifying their origin, they are placed in yards and sold in public auction in a free transaction of supply and demand.

Today, the cattle market in Buenos Aires has a capacity of 40.000 animals and sells around 2 million animals a year. It is the largest cattle market in the world.

Meat Industry

Meat at the slaughterhouse

The first methods used in the Río de la Plata region to preserve meat for export were three: *tasajo, charque* and cured meat.

Tasajo is the combination of dried meat cut into long, thin pieces and then cured in salted water. *Charque* and cured meat are thin long pieces of meat dried in the sun.

These products were exported for the first time as early as 1602. The total amount of meat sold was 500 *quintales* (1 *quintal* = 46 kg) and the destination was Cuba, according to a certificate of the time.

In 1780, a new methodology of preserving meat was introduced: salting. Ten years later great quantities of salted meat were exported from the port of Buenos Aires to Cuba and Spain.

Selecting cuts

Meat was not only in great demand by the domestic market, but salted meat was exported in big quantities as well. Meat had already become a profitable good. The farmers not only sold leather and tallow but meat as well, which was no longer a worthless product.

Only with this incentive, the breeders started importing bulls and pedigree cows to improve their live-

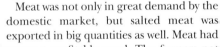

stock. This happened even before the refrigeration system started being used in the ships that carried meat to Europe.

Packed meat ready to be exported

In 1873, Charles Tellier announced in the French Academy, that his investigations about refrigeration, started some time before, had achieved full success. The steamboat "Le Frigorifique" sailed from Rouen to Buenos Aires for the first time in 1876.

Argentina immediately took advantage of these new possibilities and this new way of commercialisation and the governments of President Domingo F. Sarmiento and of President Nicolás Avellaneda, favoured the development of the chilled beef industry. During President Avellaneda's government a law was passed that exempted meat from paying export tax during five years. Since then, the quantities of meat exported did not stop growing and the modern crafts favoured the exports of Argentine meat to distant countries in the world.

In 1883, "The River Plate Fresh Meat Co. Ltd." settled in the City of Campana, on the banks of the Río Paraná. The first shipment of this company to London was a consignment of frozen rams, which arrived in excellent condition at its destination port.

"La Negra" was the next meat processing plant, which started its activity in 1885. Since then, numerous processing plants were established. The growth of domestic consumption increased as well, thus enlarging the market possibilities.

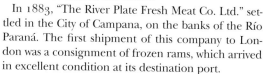

Product of "La Negra", 1940

British breeds for all climates

Argentine Meat in the World

"Argentine meat in London" c. 1925

Argentine meat exports have a significant value of the total exports of all agricultural goods.

The Hilton Share granted by Europe to meat-exporting countries applies to chilled and deboned cuts, from animals that are between 22 and 24 months old, fattened with grass and with a weight of not more than 460 kg.

They are sent in special boxes called Special Beef Boxes, authorised to have a label with the initials "sc", Special Cuts.

Strip loin, rump and tenderloin are the cuts included in these boxes.

There are three additional cuts of the round: topside, silverside and knuckle and the cube roll from the fore shank and brisket.

Our main international markets in Europe for the "*Cuota Hilton*" are: Germany, Great Britain, Holland, Italy, Belgium, Spain, France, Luxembourg, Denmark and Greece. Fresh meat is also exported to countries of the American Continent: the United States, Canada, Chile, Brazil, Bolivia, Peru and Dutch Antilles.

There are other countries, such as Iran, Israel, Singapore and Hong Kong, that also buy our meat.

"Exporting chilled beef" c. 1910

Organic meat is sent to Belgium, Germany and Italy.

Meat Characteristics

The two types of breeds, precocious and late developers, determine the characteristics of meat regarding its tenderness, colour and flavour.

The precocious breeds have a faster rate of weight gain and mature size and the result is a more tender meat. British breeds and the crossing among them and on Continental breeds belong to the first type. The Indian races, such as the Zebu and their crossings, belong to the second type.

Nicolás García Uriburu
"Taureau et Pampa"

The more it takes an animal to develop, the more it exercises and the stronger its musculature is. This generates more fibrous and less tender meat.

There are also racial differences in the marbling, which consists of thin streaks of fat in the meat within the muscular fibres, and in the covering fat that contribute towards a better taste.

Sex also influences the quality of meat although in a smaller degree than race. The male animal and the young female that has not given birth have practically the same meat quality. The hormonal changes during gestation and suckling alter the quality and the colour of the meat, there is then a difference between the meat of a young castrated bull and a heifer, and the meat of a cow.

The castrated young bull has no hormonal action, and hence its muscular mass is softer, it is also meeker and its meat is of better quality. Age is also related to muscular firmness, so the meat of a younger animal is more tender than the meat of an older one. Animals of 18 to 24 months have the best meat. It is tender, firm and it has consistent fat. From the chemical point of view, meat is made up of proteins, fat, vitamins of the B group, minerals, iron and zinc, and water.

Argentine meat does not produce cholesterol because of the traditional methods used for fattening.

Meat is a source of iron and zinc which plays an essential part in the diet of human beings. Besides, protein deficiency will affect the normal mental development of children causing attention problems, inactivity and apathy.

The Asado Tradition

Esteban Gonnet
"Gauchos eating"
c. 1860

Asados are eaten throughout the country. On Sundays at home, along the banks of the Río de la Plata, for lunch at a construction site, or in the countryside. There is always an excuse for a good asado.

*1 Rump,
2 Tenderloin, 3 Strip loin, 4 Cube roll,
5 Chuck, 6 Round,
7 Flank, 8 Knuckle,
9 Short plate,
10 Breast, 11 Brisket,
12 Fore shank*

Charles Darwin described the rite of the *asado* (barbecue) 190 years ago. In his diary on board the HMS *Beagle*, he said: "It was admirable to see with what dexterity St. Jago dodged behind the beast, till at last he contrived to give the fatal touch to the main tendon of the hind leg; after which, without much difficulty, he drove his knife into the head of the spinal marrow, and the cow dropped as if struck by lightning. He cut off pieces of flesh with the skin to it, but without any bones, sufficient for our expedition. We then rode on to our sleeping-place, and had for supper "carne con cuero," or meat roasted with the skin on it. This is as superior to common beef as venison is to mutton. A large circular piece taken from the back is roasted on the embers with the hide downwards and in the form of a saucer, so that none of the gravy is lost. If any worthy alderman had supped with us that evening, "carne con cuero," without doubt, would soon have been celebrated in London".

Retail Cuts

After the animal has been slaughtered and flayed it is divided into two halves and this is how it is sold to butcheries and supermarkets. In Argentina the animals are separated following anatomical cuts, the Europeans follow another criterion.

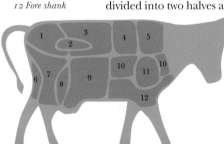

Cooking with Meat

The country can be devided according to the way meat is prepared. In south and central Argentina, meat is roasted, in the North it is boiled.

Epaminondas Chiama (1844-1921) "Horsemen from Buenos Aires"

In order to prepare a good *asado*, one has to kindle the fire with great care. A lot of hard firewood is necessary in order to produce enough embers.

After salting, the meat has to be placed on the grill or in the spit. The embers are placed around the meat and then underneath the centre of the grill, because one of the secrets of a good *asado* is time: it has to roast for quite a long time. When the juice starts oozing out, the meat has to be turned over. This is done only once. The asado is well done when the juice starts dropping again. Generally, when the meat is roasted together with the bone, then the bone has to be on the side of the embers, if it is a piece without a bone, then the side of the fat has to receive the heat from the embers.

There are three different ways of roasting meat in the countryside: the *churrasco* (a steak), or other pieces of meat, roasted directly on the grill; on a spit, stuck into the ground where the meat is roasted perpendicular to the fire. Lamb, goat's meat and pork are usually roasted on a spit.

The third way is the famous *asado con cuero* (meat with hide), which is meat roasted together with the hide, preserving all its juice and essence.

After slaughtering the animal, the meat cuts are left in the open air. On the next day, very early in the morning, a big fire has to be lit and then the meat is very slowly roasted on huge grills over the embers.

The meat is put in such a way that the hide covers the meat. The *asado con cuero* is ready when the hair of the hide is pulled and comes off easily.

There is another way of preparing an *asado con cuero*: the meat is placed with the hide on the grill, so that the hide is roasted. It can be eaten either hot or cold. The meat prepared in this way is very tender and has an exquisite taste.

George Corbett
"Asado in an estancia"
c. 1860

All Argentines know not only how to cook meat but the usually know about the different cuts and its uses as well.

The cuts used for an *asado* are the ribs, the round steak, flank steak and offal such as sweetbread, blood sausages, small intestines, kidneys.

The Argentine *puchero* is a rich stew. Meat, its most important ingredient, is boiled in salted water together with potatoes, pumpkin, sweet potatoes, carrots, corncobs and peas.

Carbonada is cooked in oil. Meat is cut in small pieces to which tomatoes, pumpkin, potatoes, sweet potatoes, corncobs and then rice and peeled peaches are added. Salt and pepper are added shortly before it is ready.

Locro, a thick, creamy soup, is made of meat, hominy, streaky bacon, pork, and sausages together with sweet potatoes, pumpkin and salt. *Locro* is served with a hot sauce which consists of chopped onions, scallions, ground pepper and paprika and salt.

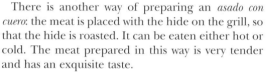

Index